WHITNEY

Exclusive Distributors:
Music Sales Limited
8/9 Frith Street,
London W1V 5TZ, England.
Music Sales Pty Limited
120 Rothschild Avenue,
Rosebery, NSW 2018,
Australia.

This publication is not authorised for sale in
the United States of America and/or Canada.

Order No. AM935737
ISBN 0-7119-5562-X
This book © Copyright 1996 by Wise Publications

Compiled by Peter Evans
Designed by Pearce Marchbank, Studio Twenty
Quarked by Ben May

Printed in the United Kingdom by
Caligraving Limited, Thetford, Norfolk.

Your Guarantee of Quality
As publishers, we strive to produce
every book to the highest commercial standards.
This book has been carefully designed to minimise awkward
page turns and to make playing from it a real pleasure.
Particular care has been given to specifying acid-free,
neutral-sized paper made from pulps which have not been
elemental chlorine bleached. This pulp is from farmed sustainable
forests and was produced with special regard for the environment.
Throughout, the printing and binding have been planned
to ensure a sturdy, attractive publication
which should give years of enjoyment.
If your copy fails to meet our high standards,
please inform us and we will gladly replace it.

Music Sales' complete catalogue describes thousands of titles
and is available in full colour sections by subject,
direct from Music Sales Limited. Please state your areas of
interest and send a cheque/postal order for £1.50 for postage to:
Music Sales Limited, Newmarket Road,
Bury St. Edmunds, Suffolk IP33 3YB.

Visit the Internet Music Shop at
http://www.musicsales.co.uk

Wise Publications
London/New York/Paris/Sydney/Copenhagen/Madrid

HOUSTON

HOW WILL I KNOW

WORDS & MUSIC BY GEORGE MERRILL, SHANNON RUBICAM & NARADA MICHAEL WALDEN

-er we meet. ____ I'm ask-in' you, 'cause you know a-bout these things.

How will I know if he's think-in' of ____ me? I try to phone, but I'm

too shy. (Can't speak.) Fall-ing in love is so ____ bit-ter-sweet. ____

This love is strong. Why do I feel weak? 3. Oh, ____ wake I feel weak? If he loves ____

I feel weak? ____ me; if he loves ____

6

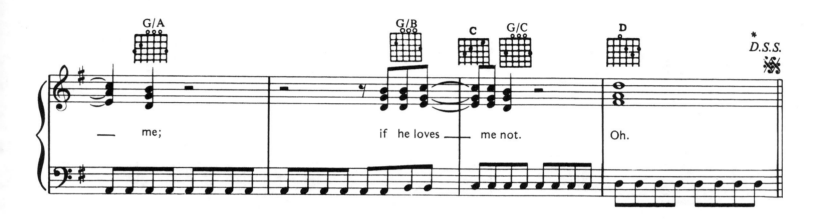

Verse 3:
Oh, wake me, I'm shakin'; wish I had you near me now.
Said there's no mistakin'; what I feel is really love.
How will I know? (Girl, trust your feelings.)
How will I know?
How will I know? (Love can be deceiving.)
How will I know?

Repeat Chorus in key of "E"

ALL AT ONCE

WORDS BY JEFFREY OSBORNE & MICHAEL MASSER
MUSIC BY MICHAEL MASSER

9

than you know,_____ so much more _____ than it shows _____ all at once.

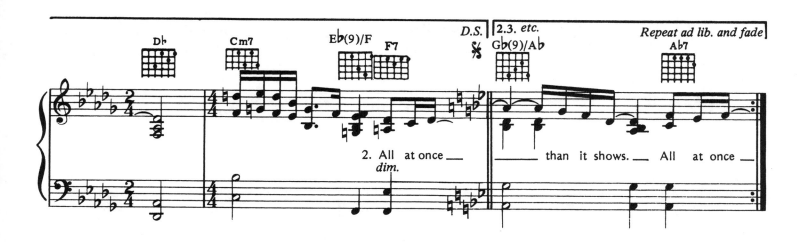

2. All at once _____ than it shows.___ All at once _____
dim.

Verse 2:
All at once
I looked around and found
That you were with another love,
In someone else's arms,
And all my dreams were shattered
All at once.
All at once
The smile that used to greet me
Brightens someone else's day.
She took your smile away,
And left me with just mem'ries
All at once.
(To Bridge:)

SAVING ALL MY LOVE FOR YOU

WORDS & MUSIC BY GERRY GOFFIN & MICHAEL MASSER

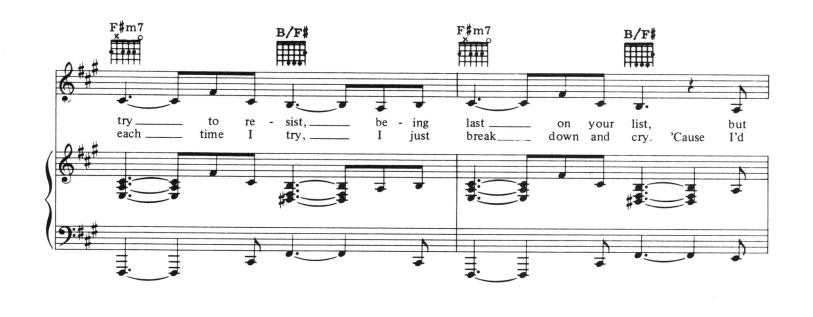

try _____ to re-sist, _____ be-ing last _____ on your list, _____ but
each _____ time I try, _____ I just break _____ down and cry. 'Cause I'd

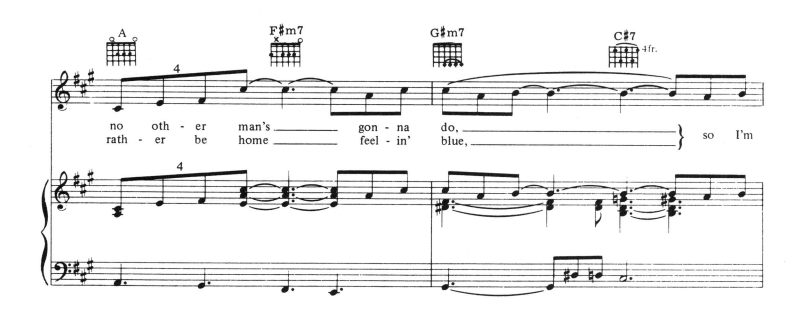

no oth - er man's _____ gon - na do, _____ } so I'm
rath - er be home _____ feel - in' blue, _____ }

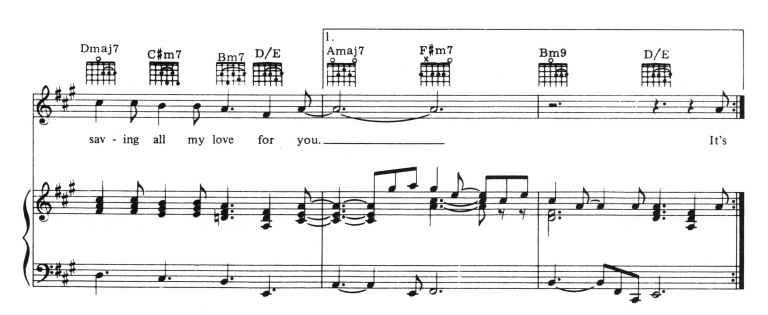

sav - ing all my love for you. _____ It's

YOU GIVE GOOD LOVE

WORDS & MUSIC BY LA FORREST COPE

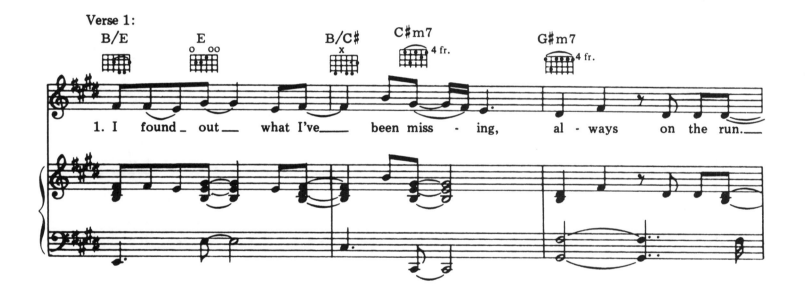

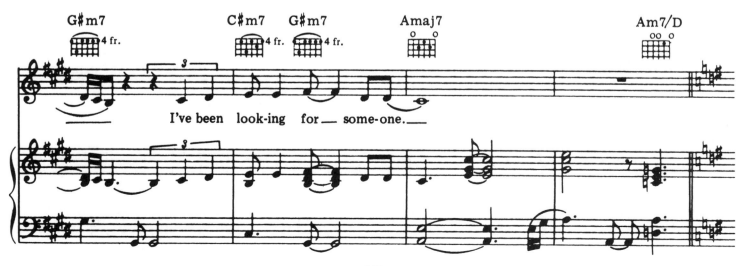

Ba-by, you give good love. ___

Verse 2:

Nev - er stop - ping, ___ I was al - ways search - ing ___ for that per - fect love, ___

the kind that girls like me ___ dream of. ___

Now you're here ___ like you've been ___ be - fore, ___ and you know ___ just what ___ I need. ___

THINKING ABOUT YOU

WORDS & MUSIC BY KASHIF & LA FORREST COPE

Medium funk (♩ = 120)

Play four times

1. I can't get you off my mind,____ no mat-ter what I do.
2. Make-be-liev-in' is a game____ that's hard for me to play.

I'm wish-ing you were here with__ me.
Don't you need me just like I need you?____

It makes no dif-f'rence, when it is____ I on-ly think of__ you.
There's no rea - son, it's just my heart that makes me feel this__ way.

Got me think-ing 'bout you.   I'm think-ing 'bout.

it too.

1. A/B   B   D.S.   **2.** A/B   B *To next strain*   **3.** A/B   *Repeat and fade*

Bridge:

Spoken: It might be pour-ing rain,   *we're like a fool, in - sane.*
I'm just a love-sick fool,   *I've got this thing for you.*   I run, I run, I run,

1. A/B

I run to you.   **2.** N.C.   I'm just a, I'm just a   love-sick fool.

cresc.   I'm just a fool.   A/B   D.S.S.

25

TAKE GOOD CARE OF MY HEART
WORDS & MUSIC BY PETER McCANN & STEVE DORFF

Chorus:

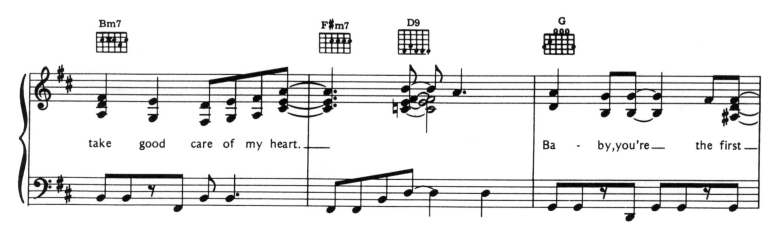

I WANNA DANCE WITH SOMEBODY
(WHO LOVES ME)

WORDS & MUSIC BY GEORGE MERRILL & SHANNON RUBICAM

Verse 2:
I've been in love and lost my senses
Spinning through the town.
Sooner or later the fever ends,
And I wind up feeling down.
I need a man who'll take a chance
On a love that burns hot enough to last.
So when the night falls,
My lonely heart calls.
(To Chorus:)

Verse 3:
I need a man who'll take a chance
On a love that burns hot enought to last.
So when the night falls,
My lonely heart calls.
(To Chorus:)

31

DIDN'T WE ALMOST HAVE IT ALL
WORDS & MUSIC BY MICHAEL MASSER & WILL JENNINGS

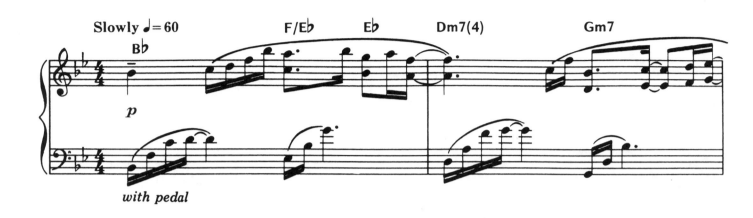

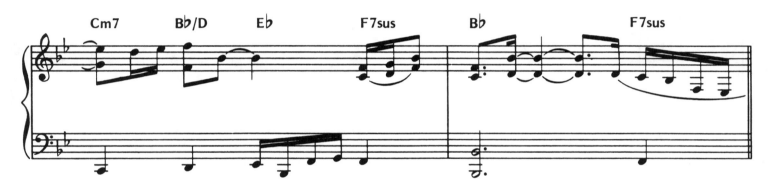

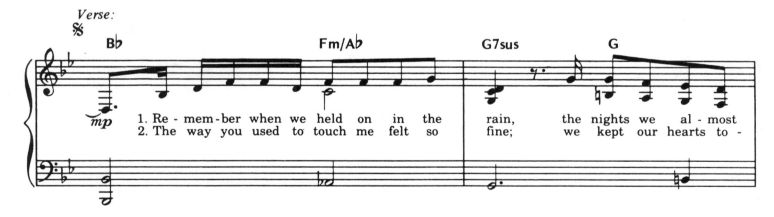

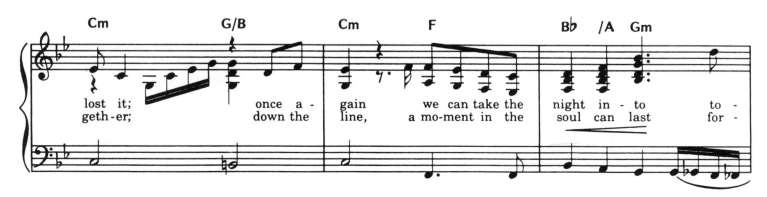

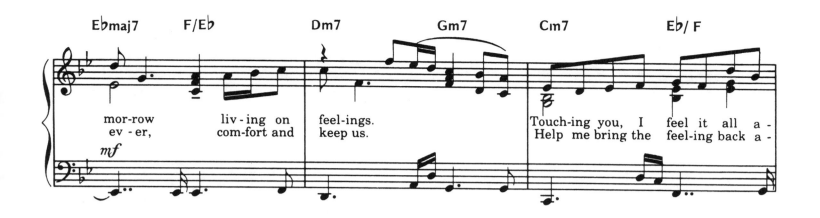

Ebmaj7 F/Eb Dm7 Gm7 Cm7 Eb/F

mor-row liv-ing on feel-ings. Touch-ing you, I feel it all a-
ev - er, com-fort and keep us. Help me bring the feel-ing back a-

mf

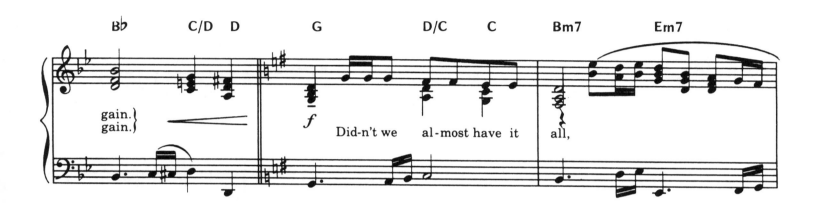

Bb C/D D G D/C C Bm7 Em7

gain.⎫
gain.⎭ f Did-n't we al-most have it all,

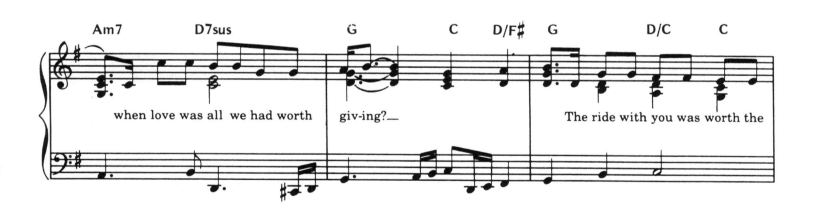

Am7 D7sus G C D/F# G D/C C

when love was all we had worth giv-ing?— The ride with you was worth the

Bm7 Em7 Am7 Dsus G Eb/F F

fall, my friend; — lov-ing you makes life worth liv-ing.—

times, when love_was young and new? Could-n't we reach_in-side and find the world of me and

you? We'll nev-er lose it a-gain,— 'cause once you know what love is, you

D.S.S.

nev-er let it end.

Coda

did-n't we al-most have it

all?

Did-n't we al-most have it all?

molto rit. & dim.

Ped.

WHERE DO BROKEN HEARTS GO?

WORDS & MUSIC BY FRANK WILDHORN & CHUCK JACKSON

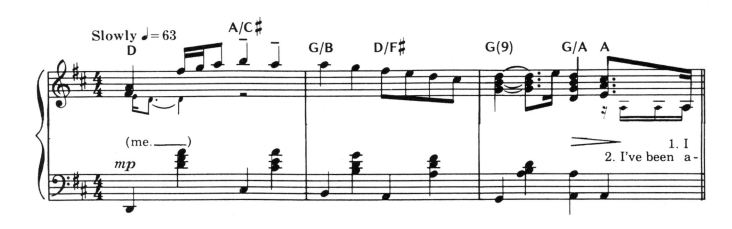

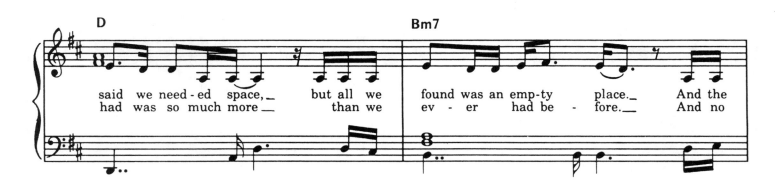

on - ly things I learned   is that I / need you des - p'rate - ly.___ } So
mat - ter now I try,   you're / al - ways on ___ my mind.___

here I__ am, ___   and / can you please_tell ___ me: ___   oh ___

Chorus:

Where do bro-ken hearts go; / can they find their__ way__home / back to the o - pen arms of a

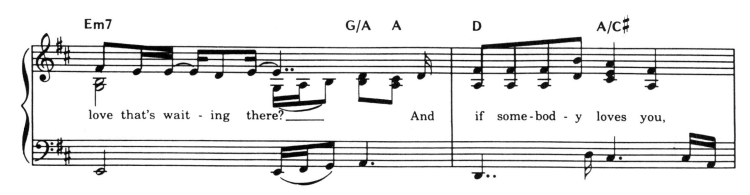

love that's wait - ing there?___   And / if some-bod - y loves you,

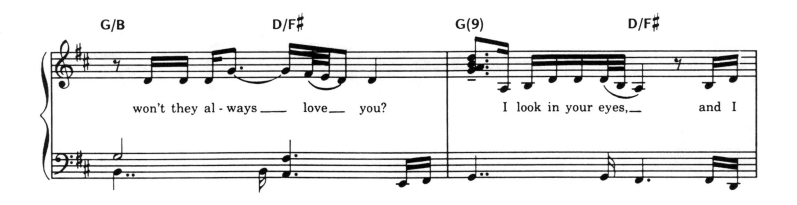

won't they al-ways ___ love ___ you?   I look in your eyes, ___   and I

know that you _ still care ___ for   know that you _ still care ___ for   me. ___   And

Bridge:

now that I ___ am here with you, ___   I'll ___ nev-er let you go. ___   I

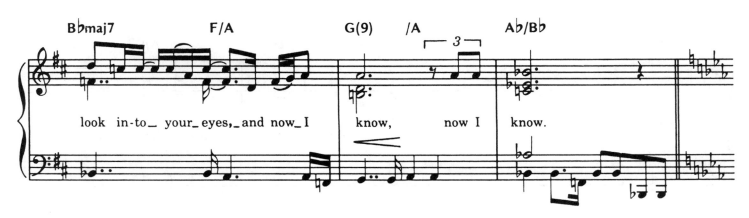

look in-to ___ your_ eyes, _ and now _ I   know,   now I   know.

ONE MOMENT IN TIME

WORDS & MUSIC BY ALBERT HAMMOND & JOHN BETTIS

I WILL ALWAYS LOVE YOU

WORDS & MUSIC BY DOLLY PARTON

RECITE:

I hope life treats you kind,
and I hope you have all that you ever dreamed of,
and I wish you joy and happiness,
but above all this, I wish you love.

SING:

And I WILL ALWAYS LOVE YOU,
I WILL ALWAYS LOVE YOU,
I WILL ALWAYS LOVE YOU,
And I WILL ALWAYS LOVE YOU,
I WILL ALWAYS LOVE YOU,
I WILL ALWAYS LOVE YOU,

SO EMOTIONAL

WORDS & MUSIC BY BILLY STEINBERG & TOM KELLY

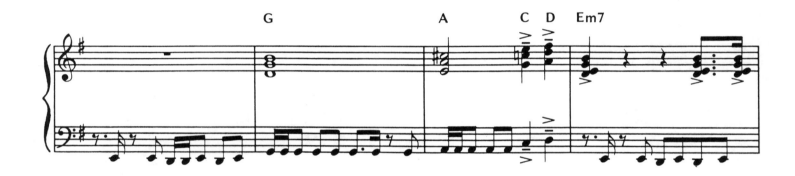

1. I've been hear-ing your heart-beat in-side of me; I keep your pho-to-graph be-

side my bed.___ Liv-ing in a world of fan-ta-sies,___ I can't get you out of my head.__

I've been wait-ing for the phone to ring all night. why you wan-na make me feel __ so good. __ I got a love of my own, __

ba - by; I should-n't get so hung up on you. __ __ I re-

mem - ber the way __ that we touch; __ I wish __ I did __ n't like __ it so

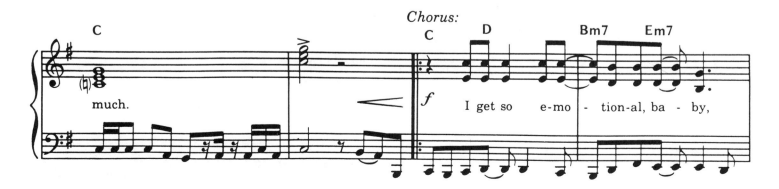

much. I get so e-mo - tion-al, ba - by,

ev-ery time _ I think _ of you. ___ I get so e-mo - tion-al, ba - by; ain't it

shock-ing what love _ can do? _ Ain't it shock-ing what love can do?_

_ Ain't it shock-ing what love can do?___ _ can do?_

Verse 2:
I gotta watch you walk in the room, baby;
I gotta watch you walk out.
I like the animal way you move,
And when you talk I just watch your mouth.

Oh, I remember the way that we touch;
I wish I didn't like it so much.

5/02 (44153)

COUNT ON ME

Words and Music by
BABYFACE, WHITNEY HOUSTON
and MICHAEL HOUSTON

Count on Me - 6 - 1

F♯m7
Bm7
2fr
Em7
nev - er gon - na end, — but you'll get through it, just
Em9/A
Chorus:
D
Em7
don't — give in. 'Cause you can count on me — through thick - and thin, a friend -
D/F♯
Gmaj13
3fr
D/A
A/G
- ship that — will nev - er end. When you — are weak, — I will — be strong, —
D(9)/F♯
G(9)
Dmaj7/F♯
Bm
help - ing you — to car - ry on. — Call on me, — I will — be there. —